The Stinky Plant

Explorer Challenge

Find out what
eats the fruit ...

D0487003

The children were in the garden.
"Come and smell this flower,"
said Mum. "It smells so sweet!"

"Look," said Wilf. "Insects like the smell of flowers, too. Shall we go back in?"

In Biff's room, the key started to glow.

It took them to a rainforest.

A man was sitting on a tree trunk.
He did not look happy.

"What is the matter?" said Wilma.

"I am a botanist," said the man.
"I collect plants."

"I am looking for one important plant.
Its flower has a strong smell."

"But I have a bad cold," said the man.
"I cannot smell at all!"

"We can help you,"
said Biff.

The children began to sniff.

Then Wilf said, "I smell something, and it is stinky!"

"Me too," said Biff. "It stinks like rotten fish!"

"That is my flower!" said the botanist.
"Come on!"

As they got nearer, the stink got stronger and stronger.

"What a fantastic flower!" said the botanist.
"What a pong!" said Wilf.

"Now we can have a proper look at it," said the botanist.

The key started to glow.
"We have to go!" said Biff.

When they got back, Wilma said, "I can still smell that plant. Shall we go out in the garden to get rid of the pong?"

They ran to the garden.
"What is that *smell*?" said Mum.

Retell the Story

Look at the pictures and retell the story in your own words.

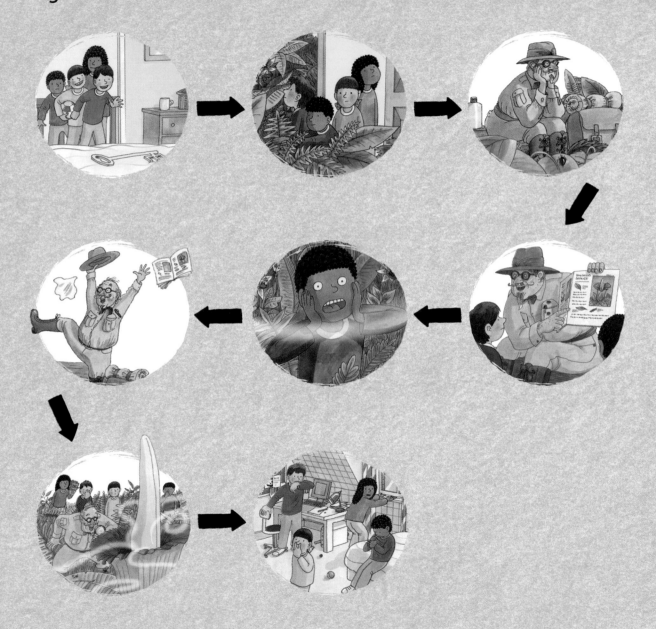

Look Back, Explorers

Where did the magic key take Biff, Chip, Wilf and Wilma?

How did the children help the botanist?

How did the botanist feel when he found the flower?

Wilf says that the flower 'smells stinky'. What other words can you think of that mean the same as *stinky*?

Did you find out what ate the fruit?

What's Next, Explorers?

Now you have been on a magic key adventure to find a stinky plant, find out all about plants ...

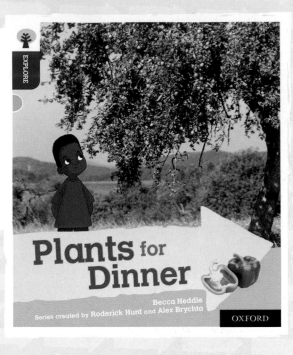

Explorer Challenge
for *Plants for Dinner*

Find out what part of the plant this is ...